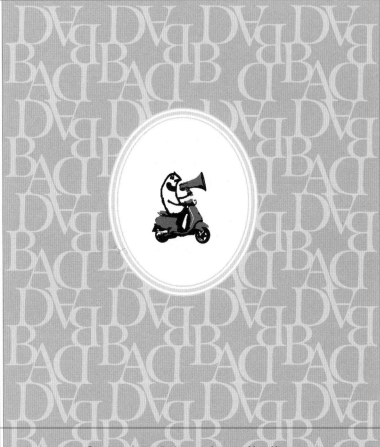

Modern Toss: PO Box 386, Brighton, BN1 3SN, United Kingdom
email: info@moderntoss.com www.moderntoss.com
First printed up in the year of 2009
Printed by Lancing Press, West Sussex, UK

A Modern Toss Publication

COLLECTED THOUGHTS

from

Drive-By Abuser

GREAT BRITAIN
2009

Sunbather

Laying out in the sun yeah
it's alright for some innit
I expect you'll get up in bit
rub on a bit of cream
re-arrange your towel
see if anyone's looking at you
then lie down for another hour
let's hope we're not relying
on cunts like you
to kickstart the economy

Telephone Box

Alright! What you doing in there?
having a piss or ringing up a prostitute?
got to be one or the other, hasn't it?
why not though, eh, it's your life, innit
ah, good luck to ya mate
see ya 'round yeah

Gastropub

Alright?
what the fuck are you then?
a restaurant or a pub?
still, get 'em pissed up enough
then they can't blame the food
while they're spraying their guts out
all over your car park

The Furrier

What you using ocelot?
got to hose the guts out first
it's only little innit
probably get an arm out of it
fiddly fucking job yeah
still, get its arsehole in the right place
and you'll be able to put a button through it
makes sense don't it

The Farmer

Alright! You a farmer yeah?
foot and mouth an'all that?
what you sellin'?
big lumps of torn-off meat?
expect you're up at half past three, aren't cha?
watching all the animals
honking and shitting themselves
good luck to ya
I couldn't fucking do it

Ready Meal

Edible shit box
with a plastic sheet on top?
got to peel it off yeah,
or pop it with a fork
you lazy fucker
survival of the fittest?
not in your case mate

Sainsburys Homebase

New branch of homebase?
that's handy
where's your shower nozzles mate?
I expect they're over the back somewhere yeah
I might come back later
do a doughnut in the car park

The Gardener

Telling all the plants where to grow?
pulling out the ones you don't like the look of
then burning 'em on a fire
not far off Pol Pot are you?
when you think about it

Power Station

Alright! you generating power
 to keep everyone's gadgets and nik naks going?
yeah, looks like it an' all
don't get me wrong, I've got the lot
computer, toaster, mp3 player
you name it, I've fucking got it
I tell you what mate, if it wasn't for you
we'd all be back in the stone age eating our own shit
not that I've got anything against that
nah, you're doing a good job mate
stick with it yeah
I'll let you get on

The Swan

You king of the ducks mate?
yeah looks like it an' all
reckon yourself a bit don't you
giving it all that with your big fucking neck
tell you what, if i ever drop me keys down the drain
you can come and fish 'em out for me
you got a business card? or shall i just look you up
under "stuck up pond toff"
see ya round yeah

The Mountaineer

Pushing yourself to the limits of human endurance
climbing up a big dirt pile?
take a picture when you get to the top
so we all know you're not bullshitting it yeah
then come back down
and wank on about it
for the rest of your life
ever tried working in an office?
doubt you're up to it mate
but someone's got to do it

France

Alright! baking a French stick, are ya?
I expect, later on, you'll be wiping your croissant
on a bit of goat's cheese won't ya?
yeah ?
eating an onion?
Quelle heure est-il ??
nah, stay where you are mate
it's all bollocks over here
alright, see ya then

Meeting

Sat in a room yeah
with some people
banging some ideas around
took four weeks to get everyone together
better think of something to say
or people will think you're fucking thick

Traffic Light

You a traffic light yeah?
yeah fucking looks like it an' all
changing colours
red, amber, green
limited range, innit
making a little beeping noise for all the blind people
nice of ya...
beep beep beep beep... green man!
oh, he's red now!
you're stuck in a rut
see ya round, yeah

TV Quipster

Quipping about things
riffing with your wit
sipping your water
everytime you get a laugh
you fucking cunt.

The Matchstick

Little strip of wood yeah
one end of you caked in phosphorus shit
sitting still as fuck in a box
twenty four seven,
three six five
waiting for the day
to get your tip scraped
against the box you live in
till your head explodes
that's life mate, don't come running to me

Alfresco Diner

Sitting at a little table on the pavement
eating a plate of food are you?
trying to look like you do it all the time
it's the new thing though innit
bit of a continental flavour yeah
any idiot can sit indoors can't they?
have to bang it down quick though
in case a bird shits on it

Ornothologist

Hiding in bushes yeah
spying on birds
ticking 'em off in a little book?
still there's no law against it is there?
be different if it was people though wouldn't it?
you'd be banged up
with all the fucking perverts.

The Tree

You a tree yeah ?!
big pole made out of wood
crawling with fucking insects
alright for some innit!
shedding your shit everywhere
hope you're gonna clear all that up
do you want a dustpan and brush?
nah, didn't think so...
what's your 'Autumn Look' gonna be?
same as last year? bunch of fucking twigs?
yeah, you carry on mate
see ya round yeah!

Airplane

Big metal tube yeah? flying around the sky
full of people shitting themselves
in case one of your wings cracks off?
what you carrying?
bunch of holiday makers
full of foreign spunk and swine flu?
let's hope they let 'em back in
I fucking wouldn't

Picnic

Having a little picnic are ya?
ham, cheese, packet of crisps..
cooler bag for it yeah?
nice day for it
why not eh?
you make me fucking sick
see ya

The Artist

Doing a painting of it are ya?
capturing the moment on canvas yeah?
what is it acrylics?
gotta sketch it out first haven't ya
then put the colours on and that
you wanna get a fucking life don't ya?
bet it looks like a stack of old shit
see ya!

Cruise Ship

Alright, you a big floating piss machine yeah?
packed out with old people on a last minute death trip
I expect most of em'll be coming back in the freezer,
won't they?
ah chuck 'em overboard mate
no one's looking

The Christmas Tree

Seasonal tree are you?
pointless existence innit
sitting round like a cunt all year
then some bloke digs you up
and puts you in a bucket
couple of weeks later
you're slung out
in a bag full of turkey fat
not much of a way
to start the new year is it?

Recycling bins

Oh hello what's going on here then?
some sort of stuck up bin meeting
glass, can, paper... pretty strict entry policy
what's all the old school rubbish meant to do?
sit out on the fucking street ?
don't get me wrong, I'm not having a go
I'm all for that green shit
if the old planet goes up the shitter
it won't be your fault for trying...
see you around yeah...

Shopping

Doing some shopping are ya?
carrying it home yeah
In some little bags?
getting it out, yeah?
sticking it on a fucking shelf ?
pay for it later love,
it's all a load of bollocks innit
whack it on the plastic!!

Golf

Mate! Oi mate!
what you playing golf are ya? yeah ?
yeah, fucking looks like it an' all
where you get the jumper from?
no, not saying?
well good luck to ya,
cos I wouldn't have the fucking nerve
tell you what, leave it eh
I'll let you get on

Wearing a hat

Wearing a hat yeah?
keeps the sun off
and tells people
that you're an arsehole
kill two birds with one stone
everyone's a winner

The Cloud

Sucking all the moisture up from one place
then randomly floating off somewhere else
and pissing it out all over the shop
without a care in the world?
you're living the dream mate

New Year Disco

Alright?
waiting for Big Ben
to tell you you've just shitted another year
of your life up the fucking wall?
still at least you're not sat indoors
watching Jools Holland lift his kilt
at Gladys Knight and the Pips

Football

Alright, football?
kicking the ball in the net
then having a little cheer and a kiss about it?
not exactly fucking chess, is it!
why not though, eh!
it's your life innit... I'll let you get on with it
'Offside!' yeah!
just kidding, I haven't got a clue mate
see ya round yeah

Brie

Big old fucking lump
of triangular fat
don't leave it out in the sun
fucking melts like a piece of shit
you have to chuck it away
that's what happened to me anyway, cheers.
(unfinished)

Reindeer

Alright! pack of reindeer yeah?
dragging a big old sack of Christmas nik-naks
while some bloke whips your arsehole with a stick?
still it's only once a year innit...

Texting

Sending a text ?
leving out som leters yeah
doing it relly fckin fast yeah
why not eh
dnt cost fuck al does it
asking someone if theyr alrght?
trns out yeah, they R
at least u fucking know
give yourself a break
or ull end up with thumb cancer
have to use ur tongue then
get all spit in the buttons

Country House

Alright mate! country house are ya?
looks like it an'all
giving it all that with your windows and columns
like some big fucking chinless shed
nice spot you got yourself, innit
who's ya owner,   Baron Lord Dave Fontleroy?
nah, made it up mate
stick with it, yeah
Rule Bri-fucking-tania!
see ya 'round !

Sunday Walk

Going for a Sunday walk?
gets you out of the house don't it
stretch your fucking legs
what's on the telly?
nothing
mind that bit of shit

The Cappucino

Think you're fucking it don't you?
little cup, half-full of hot brown shit
topped off with a lump
of frothed up cow's piss
sling on a bit of brown dust
don't sound so appealing does it?
when you put it like that
probably why you got a fancy fucking name
you stuck up cunt

Internet

Alright,
you a big digital shit cloud
of wrong information
and photos of people fucking each other?
that'd be a trip up the library
in the old days
cheers

The Jogger

What you running from?
a made up image of yourself
as the world's fattest man
tucking into a grab bag of cheese and onion
cathetered up to a bucket
and then winched out by a crane when you die...
still it's better than working
you waddling fuck

Posting a Letter

Posting a letter yeah?
sticking a bit of paper in a hole
hoping some idiot
can be bothered to deliver it?
second class?
might as well tear it up
and fucking eat it
least you get a meal out of it
I'm off to check me emails
see ya round grandad!

THE FRIENDS OF MODERN TOSS

Aled Rogers, Mandy Vaughan, Moomin Slayer, Jenni Cowdy, Ian Thatcher, Corinne Fulford, Jambive Munden, Lucie Speciale, Jonathan Parry, Lizzy Jones, Jeremy Brown, Stephen Williams, Olly Patterson, David "gamingdave" Robinson, Richard Rodeo Rhodes, Richard Milne, Matthew Lee, Nancy Paddick, Pauly & Sarah Surridge, James Matthews, Dr Marcella Eaton, Jakey Jake Jakington "Spectacular Trousers" Williams, Ruth "Yeah, fucking looks like it an' all" Tunnell, Molly 'I do like a little drink' Coath, Iain "like a BAWSE" Wilson, Nigel 'FFC' Griffiths, wooleygromit, Jamie Daykin, Gareth Baker, Chris Tnuc Sharman, Kieran Twomey, Jeff, Quirksta, Dave Triffitt, Njeri Low, Richard "Throop" Kemp, Faye Kennedy, Matthew McFadden, Alison Parr, Sarah Habershon, Stephen Hayward, Jim Christian, Joanna Wiegman, Richard Black, Darren Startup, Matthew Carter, Paul Bunton, Denzil Twocock, Paul Thomsen Kirk, Helena Mackevych, Lucy Cross, Dr. Gross, Geraint Rogers, George Withecombe, Littleroberts, Nick Jackson, Felicity Reardon, Gem Lucas, Philip Emanuel Ablethorpe, Kevin Wickett, Lee McKinnon Pederson, Ben Jordan, Chris Ashby, www.kitsch-u-like.com, Peter Horwood, Louise Burford, Sarah Wright, Sarah Roberts, Ian Funnell, Nick Hopkins, cleverlittlepod.com, Chris Mayou, Rebecca Mundon, Jeff Grant-Swan, Qwoo & Spruce! Stuart 'You alright with that yeah?' Wilson, The Third Duke of Bethnal, Graeme Patterson, Jane Skelton, NAWTY NATMAN XX, Tupper Price, Chris Plumley, Christopher Parry, Anne, Eleanor and Stevie Curran, yeah? James "writing a book are you, yeah?" Clarke, onbeschoft, Damian 'Cheese Man' Martin, Sarah Watt, dopskop, Peter Baldwin & Richard Newell, Nick & Sal, Sam Jones, Jonny Hall, Samantha Tang, Jonathan Stephens, Alexander Attwood, Stewart Killala, Mr Matt & Mrs Walter Baish-Lenz-Bannyfatter, Aaron Taylor-Cotter, Paul G Vine, Andi Fenner, Captain Billy Firebeard, Jack Brooks? Lee Franklin, Ant Farmer, Alison Walster, Colin "cONZ" Maclean, Harvey Powell, Joe & Sam Wicks, Gareth Barton, Jodie Marie Edgson, Rowan Chernin, Stephen Douchebag Martin, Meester Bond, Dani "You Wanker" Broadhead, Dignut and Grr, Thomas Cullen, Stephanie Brown, James W Harrison and Robert Crowle, Adam Martin, The Useful Idiot, Matt Ware, xBIGJOEx Freeman, Nick Price, Adam "Have it you perv" Cole, Andy Woods, NICK-MATE, Nick Kenny, Simon Fox, Amanda Wood-Jones, Paul "Jogging are you? Not much of a hobby is it?" Davies, Steves Higs, Burns & O'Shea, Mankauf, David J Wood (the), IAN GIBLIN, Sarah Thorny, Peter Griffiths, Adam "Musical Review" Croney, Suzanne Curran, Matt Lucock, Joseph N Samuel, Justin A, Tony Travis, Neil "Tango" Tandy, Shaun5Sugars, Katrina Phillips, Jon Rimmer, Neil "Pete Peters" Parker, Richard Pedrick, James & Laura Heaton, Neil Roberts, Howard Taylor, Nick Smith, Alison Dixon and Stuart Evans, Julia Barton, Dan Augey, Andy 'Thunder Cunt' Fernandez, Darren Hopton, Little Scratch, James Bates, Ashley Bates, composite, Bronyck Horrigan-Stokes, C'mon you Ebay mugs - BID! Steve Stokes, Nick Cutler, Smithtosh, Benjamin Brace, TR McGowran,

Ian, Richard Parkin, Molly Molloy, Danny Crump, Frin & Rob, "Talky Laureate" Cattell, Jane Shepherd, Jenny Walker, BARRELL & LAWLOR, Jim Gates, Richard Paul-Jones, Helen Ralley, Chris Brown, Simon Pinner, Holly Wheeler, Stephen Pinner, Mister Carter, Narelle Cunningham, Oder Rövknull Pole, Stephen Pastel, Dylan Archer, Chris Topher, Ian Humphreys, Equerry Willy Lopez the Third, Simon + Claire Hunter, Buster Gonad, Kiran Khetia, Aden Davies @aden_76, Catherine Allen, Sarah Hammond, Gareth Gamble, Matthew Cunliffe, Andy Tough, Stuart (the naked gardener) Camm, Lord Damo, Edweird Hall, Gareth Wane, Lucy Williams, Dave Miller, Selina Ellie Salkeld, Johnydee, Sir Leeroy Mullin of Cuntsville, John Matthews, Bin Gibson, James Daniel, squeakywheels, GiFi, Emmo, Graeme Langlands, Jonathan Mason, Menelas, Dr Bara Erhayiem BMedSci(Hons) BM BS MRCP, Dr James Ellison BMedSci(Hons) BM BS, Christian Eager, Matt HOOK, Denis & Anne HOOK, Relims, Mr Blue Sky, Andy + Lois, Lisa Ransom, Alan Lewis, Charles Wander, George Salmon, Robbo, Richard Company, Big Chad, riskyy, Simon Kehoe, Martin M, Simon "some sort of cunt" Arnold, Kevin Doherty, Benjamin Dodds, Lachlan Wills, Phil Whaite, Allan Taylor, Gaz Lee, Charlie MacDonald, jaime lhas read, Dr Miles G Tawell, Tiny Gibson, Rupert Evill, Jake By The Lake, Barry Worth, The (ex-) Reverend Horne, Neale & Nicky, Sajey-baby, Di Howeo, Ali Weir, Emma Cheung, robd, Simon Bottomley, Sorrel Wood, Son of Shoes, Tom Greenwood, Edmund the Wizard, BairstowDTD, "johnnyapples", Paul S J Martin, Nicole Foyster, Huntly Thomas, Amy Richardson, Tom 'nice stubble' Graham, Andy 'Barry' Chiles, Squirrel Freeman, Simon Cochrane, Carol Bulis, Dr Andrew Storey, Addie Jay's Electro Shite (myspace.com/addiejay), Alex Mann, DUNCAN TRAVIS, Mike Currie, Tim Havard, Rob Tamlin, Philippa Hawkes, Paul Cross, Rosie, Benjamin John Holt, Simon "Fuck Your Job" Bond, Thomas Everitt, Sarah Weeding, Ben Golding, Jeremy Crane, Tamborina Cocke, Colm Nolan, "Maria Kikillos, but not Matt Jones as the cunt has dumped me. Johnny Boyd, Matt Higgins, Henry Bruno Russell, MIKE STAFFORD IN CAPITALS! Peter Gooderham, Luke J Lewis, Ross Dougan, David Overton, Sam Spacey and Lil Kels, Brian "B-DOGG" Smith, Stephen Hayward, Iain Wareham, Halloway and Pierghetto, Sean Sturge, Lee Russell, Darren Smith, Beth Thomas, Robert Maclean-Eltham, Jillycross, Benito, Tom Tit-Wash, Jason Panudy, Finlay Goldring (age 4 months), Jane Allison, Adam Collings, Sarah Warrington, Gordon Ralph McHendry, Sense Worldwide, Christopher Tong, Danielle Gates, David "readin' my name yeah?" Harkin, Tigger Burton, Paul Faassen, My Wonderful Girlfriend, Will and Bertie, Dicko, Kinky Jon, Rob Honeybone, Dave Porter, Charmaine Kastner, Barry Foster, Samantha Tang, Jonathan Stephens, Pete Peters, Luke Davey, Cassie Morrison, Jason Kranzler, Matthieu GOLD, Rob Pratt, Anthony Askew, Chris Dorward, Richard Burrows, Helen "I still want paying" Dobby, Bob Cotterill, Vive la République, Alistair Testo.